FOURTH YEAR ASSESSMENT PAPERS IN

REASONING

PUPIL'S BOOK

J M BOND

Nelson

Thomas Nelson and Sons Ltd
Nelson House   Mayfield Road
Walton-on-Thames   Surrey KT12 5PL

51 York Place
Edinburgh EH1 3JD

P.O. Box 18123   Nairobi   Kenya

Yi Xiu Factory Building
Unit 05-06   5th Floor
65 Sims Avenue   Singapore 1438

Thomas Nelson (Hong Kong) Ltd
Toppan Building 10/F   22A Westlands Road
Quarry Bay   Hong Kong

Thomas Nelson (Nigeria) Ltd
8 Ilupeju Bypass   PMB 21303   Ikeja   Lagos

© **J M Bond 1977, 1983**
First published 1977
Second edition 1983
Reprinted 1984
Pupil's book ISBN 0-17-424475-4
              NCN 159-0726-1
Answer book ISBN 0-17-424476-2
              NCN 159-0727-1

By the same author
Introductory, First, Second, Third and Fourth Year
Assessment Papers in Mathematics

Introductory, First, Second, Third and Fourth Year
Assessment Papers in English

First, Second and Third Year Assessment Papers
in Reasoning

Filmset in Nelson Teaching Alphabet
by Mould Type Foundry Ltd
Brookfield Street   Preston   England

Printed in England
by Ebenezer Baylis & Son Ltd
The Trinity Press   Worcester and London

In this code shapes are used in place of letters. Here are four words and underneath them are four sets of shapes, but they are not beneath the right words. Can you sort them out?

ball	bad	bed	bale
□ ⊙ ◇	□ ○ △ △	□ ○ △ ⊙	□ ○ ◇

1 **ball** should be ....

2 **bad** should be ....

3 **bed** should be ....

4 **bale** should be ....

Put these words into the code.

5 deal ....

6 ebb ....

7 dale ....

8 lead ....

9 add ....

10 bleed ....

11 What is the fifth odd number greater than 21? ....

12 Which number is exactly half-way between 39 and 63? ....

Fill in the missing word in each of the following lines.

13	busy/bee	quiet/mouse	blind/................
14	strong/horse	slow/snail	meek/................
15	sharp/needle	sweet/honey	right/................
16	white/snow	green/grass	brown/................
17	good/gold	clean/new pin	fit/................
18	black/coal	thick/thieves	tough/................

There are five vowels: **a, e, i, o** and **u.**

19–21 Underline any of the words below which contain all these vowels.

platinum   favourite   peculiar   pineapple

equatorial   affectionate   mosquito   cauliflower

22 If you wrote all the numbers from 19 to 30 how many times would you write the figure **2**? ....

Fill in the next two numbers or sets of letters in each of the lines below.

23–24	de	gh	jk	mn	....	....
25–26	ab	ef	ij	mn	....	....
27–28	7	8	10	13	....	....

Underline the right word in the brackets.

29 Man is to woman as boy is to (child, baby, girl, lady)
30 Bee is to hive as spider is to (net, web, nest, barn)
31 Pig is to sty as snail is to (garden, soil, slug, shell)
32 Seven is to seventy as hundred is to (million, ten, seven, thousand)
33 One is to first as two is to (double, second, third, first)
34 Good is to better as bad is to (best, worst, better, worse)
35 What is the smallest number which, when divided by 4, 6 or 8, has a remainder of 3?   ....
36 Take the next even number greater than 88 from the next odd number smaller than 101.   ....

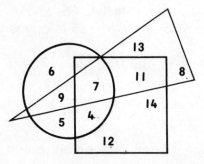

37 Find the sum of the numbers in the triangle, but not in the square. Take this number from the sum of the numbers in the square, but not in the circle.   ....
38 Add together the numbers in the triangle, but not in the circle. Take from this number the sum of the numbers in the circle only.   ....
39 Find the sum of the numbers in the square, but not in the triangle. Take from this number the sum of the numbers in the triangle only.
....

The words on each of these lines follow a pattern. Look at them carefully, and then write the next word on each line.

40	heir	her	lady	lay	pain	....
41	sloth	lot	eager	age	power	....
42	smooth	moot	brides	ride	change	....
43	stork	rot	dwarf	raw	snipe	....
44	delay	ale	stiff	fit	storm	....
45	silent	sent	minute	mute	palace	....

Three years ago John was five years old, and his mother was five times his age.

46 How old will his mother be in four years' time?   ....
47 How old will John be then?   ....

5

48 Which letter appears most frequently in the word **accommodation**?

....

Underline the word in each line which has a completely different meaning from the other words.

49 pain	discomfort	aid	suffering	distress
50 discover	detect	reveal	cover	find
51 cause	error	mistake	fault	flaw
52 tie	loosen	unite	fasten	join
53 end	finish	source	completion	conclusion
54 tutor	trainer	instructor	teacher	pupil

The houses on one side of the road are numbered from I to 35, and those on the other side of the road are numbered from 36 to 70. No. 35 is opposite to no. 36.

55 What is the number of the house which is opposite no. II?

No. ....

56 No. 23 is opposite no. ....

57 No. 31 is opposite no. ....

On each line one of the words on the left has a similar meaning to one of the words on the right. Underline both words.

58–59 ruler, strict, bent   straight, severe, sentence

60–61 second, minute, hour   tiny, time, clock

62–63 busy, thankful, lenient   lazy, merciful, tired

Put the following words in the order in which you would find them in the dictionary.

autumn   annual   ancient   August   aunt   adult

64 (1) ....   **65** (2) ....   **66** (3) ....

67 (4) ....   **68** (5) ....   **69** (6) ....

Can you sort out these jumbled words?

Vegetable soup

70 I sliced **nonoi** ....

71 I sliced **totopa** ....

72 I sliced **pinurt** ....

73 I sliced **rocart** ....

74 2 sticks of **yelerc** ....

75 I sprig of **slaryep** ....

76 I pint of **tocks** ....

77 I pinch of **slat** ....

average monthly temperature in Jerusalem

average monthly temperature in London

78 The highest monthly temperature in Jerusalem is ....

79 For how many months does Jerusalem have this temperature? ....

80 In London the highest temperature is ....

81 In July the difference between the temperatures in the two cities is ....

82 In which month is there the biggest difference in temperature between Jerusalem and London? ....

average hours of sunshine (daily)

	April	May	June	July	August	September
Jerusalem	9	11	12	12	12	10
London	6	7	7	7	6	5

83 The highest number of hours of sunshine in Jerusalem is ....

84 For how many months do they have this amount of sunshine? ....

85 The highest number of hours of sunshine in London is ....

Can you change the first word into the second word by altering one letter in each line?

86 m i l e   **87** r e a p   **88** n a m e   **89** h e a p

....

s i l k   r o a r   s o m e   t e a r

7

Here is part of a train timetable.

	Train A	Train B	Train C	Train D
Leeds	06.35	09.35	14.35	16.35
Bradford	07.00	10.00	15.00	17.00
Halifax	07.13	10.13	15.13	17.13
Hebden Bridge	07.27	10.27	15.27	17.27
Todmorden	07.35	10.35	15.35	17.35
Manchester	08.06	11.03	16.07	18.06

90 Train A takes .... to complete the journey.
91 Train B takes .... to complete the journey.
92 Train C takes .... to complete the journey.
93 Train D takes .... to complete the journey
94–95 Which two trains take the same time to do the journey? ....
96 Which train takes the longest time? ....
97 The train which takes the shortest time is ....
98–99 Between which two stations does the travelling time vary?
    (Leeds, Bradford, Halifax, Hebden Bridge, Todmorden, Manchester)
100 If I lived in Bradford and wished to be in Manchester by 10.00 a.m.
    on which train would I have to travel? ....

Underline one number in each of the three brackets to make the sum correct.
1–3 (7, 2, 4) × (3, 5, 2) = (18, 16, 12)
4–6 (9, 18, 12) ÷ (3, 4, 2) = (2, 5, 9)

Tom and Paul learn Latin and French. Paul and Tim learn French and
Spanish. John and Tom learn German and Latin.
7   Who learns Latin but not French? ....
8   Who learns French but not Spanish? ....
9   Which language does Tom not learn? ....
10 Who learns German but not French? ....
11 Which language does Paul not learn? ....
12 Who learns Latin, French and Spanish? ....

Underline one word from each set of words in brackets to give the right
answer.
13–14 Foot is to person as (mane, hoof, saddle) is to (cat, rider, horse)
15–16 Person is to house as (fish, animal, bird) is to (sea, nest, scales)
17–18 Hand is to clock as (poetry, spoke, lesson) is to (wheel, speak, verse)

19 A man went to the bank to cash a cheque. He was given new £5 notes
which were numbered consecutively from 449276 to 449373. How much
money did he get? ....
20 If Sunday is the first day of the week what are the middle letters of the
fifth day of the week? ....

On each line there are two words which have opposite meanings.
Underline both words.

21–22	blue	colour	pale	green	dark	tint
23–24	feeble	fertile	harvest	autumn	season	barren
25–26	cheap	expansive	cost	expensive	price	common

Fill in the letter which will best finish the first word and also start the second
word.
27 deb .... rod
28 the .... any
29 cas .... nee
30 fas .... hin
31 hal .... ish

32 Which letter occurs twice in **transparent**, once in **wretched** and not at
all in **insolent**? ....

33–39 Mrs. X goes to the bank to cash a cheque for £7·78. She asks if she can receive the smallest number of notes and coins possible. She receives:

.... £5 notes
.... £1 notes
.... 50p coins
.... 20p coins
.... 10p coins
.... 5p coins
.... 2p coins
.... 1p coins
.... $\frac{1}{2}$p coins

There is one word on each line which cannot be formed from the letters of the word on the left (using each letter once only). Underline that word.

40	**reduction**	notice	direct	deduct	toured	ironed
41	**description**	potion	prone	prince	credit	notice
42	**character**	archer	earth	crater	charter	teacher
43	**purchases**	shares	cheeps	spruce	arches	sharp
44	**concentrate**	trace	concrete	contents	accent	trance
45	**atmosphere**	heroes	phrase	stream	spread	master

On each line three pairs of words have similar meanings, but one pair have opposite meanings. Underline that pair.

46	regret/sorrow	option/choice	host/guest	feeble/weak
47	doctor/patient	test/try	glance/look	coarse/rough
48	terror/fear	moan/groan	sleek/smooth	speak/listen
49	withdraw/retire	accuse/blame	curb/control	guilt/innocence
50	accept/refuse	divide/share	inquire/ask	transparent/clear
51	vanquish/defeat	extend/enlarge	deluge/drought	custom/habit

The following are times of trains between Appleton and Bakewell. Fill in the missing figures in the chart.

		Leaves Appleton	Journey lasts	Arrives at Bakewell
52	Train A	09.53	.... minutes	10.28
53	Train B	10.17	45 minutes	....
54	Train C	11.49	42 minutes	....
55	Train D	12.19	.... minutes	13.12

56 Which is the fastest train? ....
57 Which is the slowest? ....

Fill in the missing figures in these sums.

58–60
```
    3 6....
    2....9
  +....7 8
  ─────────
  1 1 9 4
```

61–64
```
    6....1 3
  − 1 4 5....
  ──────────
    ....5....6
  ──────────
```

65–68
```
    5....9....
  ×        6
  ──────────
    3....7....4
  ──────────
```

69–70
```
        1 5 7....
  5 ) 7....9 5
```

Here are some long words, and, on the right of the page, some shorter words which have the same meaning. They are not in the right order. Can you sort them out?

71 **enigma** means ....   mock
72 **opulent** means ....   underground
73 **elliptical** means ....   oval
74 **immaculate** means ....   sitting
75 **colossal** means ....   puzzle
76 **indolent** means ....   rich
77 **subterranean** means ....   huge
78 **deride** means ....   lazy
79 **sedentary** means ....   spotless

        diction   action   notion   emotion

If these four words are spelled backwards and then put into alphabetical order, which will be:

80 the first? ....
81 the last? ....

        meant   tent   consent   comment

If these four words are spelled backwards and then put into alphabetical order, which will be:

82 the second? ....
83 the third? ....

Key

Victoria line	
Central line	
Circle line	
District line	
Metropolitan line	
Northern line	
Bakerloo line	
Piccadilly line	
Jubilee line	

MARBLE ARCH · BOND STREET · OXFORD CIRCUS · QUEENSWAY · LANCASTER GATE · GREEN PARK · LEICESTER SQUARE · HYDE PARK CORNER · PICCADILLY CIRCUS · KNIGHTSBRIDGE · CHARING CROSS

84 How many lines pass through Green Park? .... lines
85 If I go from Green Park to Charing Cross I will go on the .... line.
86 Queensway is on the .... line.
87 Name the station between Bond Street and Lancaster Gate.

....

See how quickly you can do these:

88 248×50

89 306×50

....

....

90 188×50

91 232×50

....

....

In a certain code the word **surgeon** is written **4783652**. In this code:

92 **3526** is ....

93 **5784** is ....

94 **8546** is ....

95 **85376** is ....

96 **4552** is ....

97 **27846** is ....

98 If I had 7 more books I would have half as many as Charles. I have 15. How many has Charles? .... books
99 In two years time I will be three times as old as my brother who is 2. How old am I now? .... years
100 When I am 13 he will be .... years

Paper 3

One word is different in some way from the other words in the line.
Underline that word.

1	sword	pistol	spear	dagger	lance
2	hen	duck	goose	cow	bull
3	team	players	gang	horde	herd
4	cub	puppy	sow	fawn	calf
5	grunts	croaks	purrs	gallops	bellows
6	less	latest	best	least	most

7 Which letter is in **paint** but not in **pantry**? ....
8 Which letter is in **principle** but not in **principal**? ....
9 Which letter is in **pedestal** but not in **pedestrian**? ....
10 Which letter is in **response** but not in **resonance**? ....
11 Which letter is in **peculiar** but not in **pecuniary**? ....
12 Which letter is in **contingent** but not in **continue**? ....

13–17 Underline the words in which three vowels appear next to each other.
   agreeable   believe   luscious   heinous   bureau
   radius   eloquence   ingenuous   beetroot   piteous

A concert was held on three days: February 27th, 28th and 29th.
18 In which year was the concert?   (1982, 1984, 1985, 1987)
19 Two days after tomorrow is Saturday. Which day was the day before yesterday? ....
20 If the months were put in alphabetical order, which would be the last month? ....
21 Which would be the 6th month? ....
22 If the days were put in alphabetical order which would be the first day? ....
23–24 Counting Sunday as the first day of the week, which days have the same position alphabetically as they have in the week?

   ....

Underline the pair of words which have opposite meanings.

25	whole/total	increase/enlarge	heal/hurt
26	obey/command	earn/gain	map/plan
27	busy/alert	dear/expensive	common/rare
28	consent/dissent	omen/sign	frank/candid
29	excess/surplus	entrance/exit	famous/renowned

Underline the word which rhymes with the word on the left.

30	**rough**	cough	cuff	laugh	how	through
31	**dough**	through	bough	enough	foe	tough
32	**bawl**	trail	bail	wool	sale	fall
33	**heir**	here	fur	dare	ear	weir
34	**tier**	fear	heir	fare	fire	sir

What relation is:

35 Mrs. Andrews to her son's daughter? ....

36 Mrs. Bell to her father's brother? ....

37 Mrs. Collins to her sister's brother? ....

38 Tom to his father's mother? ....

39 Jane to her brother's wife? ....

Underline one word from each section in brackets to make a sensible sentence.

40–42 (Steven, Anne, the baby) found the (rattle, dog, book) in her (desk, hut, bottle).

43–45 (Seven, four, ten) plus (six, eight, five) equals (nine, eleven, fourteen).

46–48 (Thames, Pacific, London) is a (city, lake, ocean) in (Scotland, England, France).

49–51 A (dog, rose, oak) is a (tree, bush, flower) which blooms in (winter, summer, spring).

52–54 The (postman, gardener, grocer) (dug, delivered, drove) the (counter, flower, letter).

In each space write the missing number.

55	18	13	9	6	....	3
56	60	48	38	....	24	20
57	3	8	14	21	29	....
58	....	12	18	25	31	38
59	11	13	12	15	....	17

Arrange these famous people in order of age by numbering them in the brackets. Put the eldest first.

60	Margaret Thatcher	born 1925	( )
61	Eric Morecambe	born 1926	( )
62	Frankie Howerd	born 1921	( )
63	Michael Crawford	born 1942	( )
64	Sir Harold Wilson	born 1916	( )
65	Albert Finney	born 1936	( )

House of Hanover	Reign
George I	1714–1727
George II	1727–1760
George III	1760–1820
George IV	1820–1830
William IV	1830–1837
Victoria	1837–1901

66 For how many years did these kings and queens reign altogether?

....

67 Who was on the throne at the end of the nineteenth century?

....

68 Who was on the throne at the end of the eighteenth century?

....

69 Napoleon died in 1821. In whose reign was this?   ....

70 The Battle of Trafalgar was in 1805. Who was reigning then?

....

71 Sir Christopher Wren died in 1723. How long had George I been king?

....

72 Which monarch reigned for the shortest time?   ....

73 Victoria was 18 when she came to the throne. Who was king when she was born?   ....

Here is a chart showing the cost of some holidays to Holland.

1 week			2 weeks		
Departure date	Return date	Price	Departure date	Return date	Price
July 3rd	July 10th	£120	July 3rd	July 17th	£220
July 10th	July 17th	£120	July 10th	July 24th	£220
July 17th	July 24th	£130	July 17th	July 31st	£230
July 24th	July 31st	£130	July 24th	August 7th	£230

74 If I have a 2 week holiday starting on July 17th it will cost: ....

75 What will be the cost for two people to have a week's holiday starting on July 10th?   ....

76 How much would it cost for one person to have a fortnight's holiday starting on July 10th?   ....

77 How much would a family of three people save by having 2 weeks' holiday starting on July 3rd rather than waiting until July 17th?

....

78 How much more does it cost to stay 2 weeks than 1 week?   ....

Here is part of a train timetable.

	Chester	Euston	
Train A	**07.18**	**10.00**	
Train B	09.10	11.54	
Train C	**10.28**	**13.14**	SO A
Train D	11.10	14.10	
Train E	**14.38**	**17.23**	SX
Train F	15.15	18.03	

Heavy type denotes "through" trains; otherwise trains stop at Crewe.
SO   Saturdays only
SX   Mondays to Fridays
A   May to September

79   Which is the first train to stop at Crewe?   ....
80   Train .... doesn't run on Saturdays.
81   Which of these trains runs only in the summer?   ....
82   Does Train F stop at Crewe?   ....
83   How many "through" trains are there per day?   ....
84   How many trains are there any day in the winter?   ....

The words on each of the following lines follow a pattern. Can you fill in the missing word?

85	bird	bride	part	prate	cart	crate	salt	....
86	write	wit	tread	tea	stone	son	speak	....
87	cheap	cap	avoid	aid	bread	bad	plain	....
88	clear	arc	loyal	all	abuse	sea	anger	....
89	what	hate	shop	hope	glut	lute	drop	....

Find a letter which will finish the first word and also start the second word.

90   hal .... ish
91   als .... nce
92   sol .... ven
93   mic .... ach

94   Which number is exactly half-way between 44 and 80?   ....

16

English numbers: I   2   3   4   5   6   7   8   9

Egyptian numbers: I   Ꭲ   Ꝿ   Ɛ   O   Ɣ   V   ᐱ   ٩

95–96 Which Egyptian numbers are similar to some of our numbers but do not have the same value?   ....

97–98 Which Egyptian numbers are like ours and have the same value?   ....

99 Which Egyptian number is like the Roman numeral 5?   ....

100 Which Egyptian number is a mirror reflection of one of ours?   ....

Below are some proverbs. On each line the letters of one of the words have been jumbled up. In the space write the word as it should be spelled.

1 A **gnllior** stone gathers no moss. ....

2 Beggars can't be **serchoos**. ....

3 Don't count your **skinecch** before they are hatched.

....

4 **hengou** is as good as a feast. ....

5 Exchange is no **royberb**. ....

6 Familiarity breeds **tentcomp**. ....

7 Fine **eheatsfr** make fine birds. ....

Jane has a £10 book token. Here are some of the books she likes. Which books does she buy if she spends £10 exactly?

Schoolgirls' annual	£3·50
Horses	£2·25
Pocket book of birds	£2·40
Top ten annual	£2·80
On the farm	£1·85
Stamp collecting	£0·50

8–11 Jane buys:

....

One word or number is, in some way, different from the others on the line. Underline it.

12	oak	ash	beech	pine	elm
13	daffodil	primrose	violet	tulip	catkin
14	83	63	33	36	18
15	49	56	79	28	63
16	chair	stool	bench	form	table
17	church	hall	chapel	cathedral	abbey

The words on each line follow a pattern. Look for it and then complete each line.

18	sword	words	spick	picks	stuck	....
19	steam	seam	steal	seal	brass	....
20	motor	rot	straw	war	order	....
21	garnet	ant	wearer	err	circle	....
22	friend	red	assist	sit	admire	....
23	centre	ten	create	are	please	....

Underline the smallest and put a ring round the largest number on each line.

24–25	413 250	413 025	413 205	423 125	423 521
26–27	87 659	87 679	87 695	86 796	86 759
28–29	31 205	32 150	31 250	32 105	32 125

a b c d e f g h i j k l m n o p q r s t u v w x y z

Arrange the letters of the alphabet so that the vowels are first, followed by the consonants.

30 Which is now the tenth letter? ....
31 Which is now the twenty-first letter? ....
32 How many letters are in the same place in this alphabet as they are in the proper alphabet? ....
33 In which place is letter **b**? ....
34 Which letter is just before **b**? ....
35 How many letters are there between **h** and **p**? ....

Choose one of the words from the column on the right of the page to best fill each space.

36 The match .... in a draw.   rescued
37 The best seats were .... for the parents.   restored
38 The lady .... at Holt Hall.   resulted
39 The lifeboat .... the sailors.   resigned
40 The headmaster was .... by all the village.   resided
41 The traffic was .... to one side of the road.   reserved
42 The craftsman .... the old table.   respected
43 The teacher .... at the end of the term.   restricted

Underline the two words on each line which have similar meanings.

44–45	famous	name	person	renowned	rich
46–47	lure	fear	power	dread	firm
48–49	cause	cross	disorder	choose	pick

The first word in each line can be changed into the second word in three stages, by altering one letter at a time. Can you fill in the first two stages?

50–51	take	....	....	live
52–53	pipe	....	....	hill
54–55	good	....	....	work
56–57	home	....	....	ripe

In Roman numerals **V** = 5, **X** = 10, **L** = 50.

58	XXVIII	=	....	59	XLII	=	....	60	XXIV = ...
61	XXXIX	=	....	62	LI	=	....	63	LXXV = ...

64 Which letter appears once in **matinee**, twice in **dungeon** and three times in **pronunciation**? ....

A–C	D–E	F–I	J–M	N–P	Q–R	S–T	U–Z
1	2	3	4	5	6	7	8

Here is a set of encyclopaedias.
In which volumes would you find details of the following?

65 Parliament   Volume ....
66 Kings of England Volume ....
67 Bees   Volume ....
68 Saints   Volume ....
69 Diamonds   Volume ....
70 Owls   Volume ....
71 Gold   Volume ....
72 West Indies   Volume ....

Here are some mapping signs.

wood   park   heathland

quarry   open pit   orchard

Draw each sign in the correct square:

73 a wood in C4
74 a quarry in B1
75 a park in E3
76 an orchard in A4
77 heathland in D2
78 an open pit in A2

To multiply by 25, you add two noughts and then divide by 4.

Example: $40 \times 25 = 4000 \div 4 = 1000$

79 36×25

....

80 44×25

....

81 64×25

....

82 48×25

....

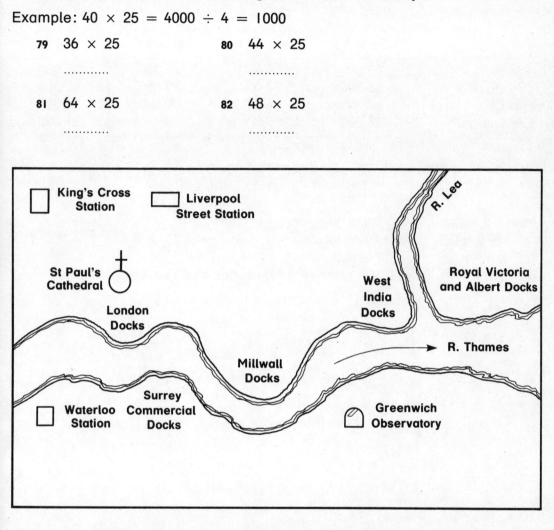

83 In which direction does the River Thames flow? ....
84 Is St. Paul's Cathedral north or south of the river? ....
85 How many stations are north of the Thames? ....
86 How many stations are south of the Thames? ....
87 How many docks are on the south bank of the river? ....
88 How many are on the north bank? ....
89 Greenwich Observatory is (N, S, E, W) of the West India Docks.

90–94 I owe Timothy 87p. I want to repay him with as few coins as possible. How can I do this?

.... 50p .... 20p .... 10p .... 5p 2p

Here is a "Top of the Pops" chart. It shows how many records each group sold each week in June.

	1st week	2nd week	3rd week	4th week
Agony	45 000	56 000	29 000	27 000
The Boxers	35 000	37 000	40 000	43 000
The Cats	42 000	44 000	39 000	29 000
The Dodgers	28 000	25 000	43 000	51 000

95   Which group sold more records each week? ....

96–97   Which groups were top for two weeks running?

....

98   Which group was top in the fourth week? ....

99   Which group rose from bottom to top of the chart in the four weeks?

....

100   Which group sold the most records during the four weeks?

....

Paper 5

Complete the following table:

	Train leaves at	Journey lasts	Train arrives at
1	09.37	....	10.21
2	10.41	38 minutes	....
3	....	51 minutes	12.05
4	12.27	....	13.02
5	13.29	47 minutes	....
6	....	1 hour 9 minutes	15.05

Find a word which could be put in front of the other words on the line to form a compound word or a pair of words that go together.

7	boat	buoy	guard	jacket	....
8	way	proof	pistol	mark	....
9	guard	man	escape	drill	....
10	cutter	lark	pecker	worm	....

Put the following words in alphabetical order.

stripe   string   stripling   strike   strip   stringent

11 (1) ....   12 (2) ....   13 (3) ....

14 (4) ....   15 (5) ....   16 (6) ....

Underline the item which is the second largest in each group.

17	chapter	word	paragraph	letter	sentence
18	thousand	million	one	hundred	ten
19	hour	week	second	day	minute
20	most	few	more	least	some
21	town	county	street	country	village
22	68	135	89	210	23
23	cat	cow	mouse	sheep	dog

One word on each line cannot be formed from the letters of the word on the left (using each letter once only). Underline it.

24	**instalment**	stint	stain	meat	later	last
25	**stratagem**	stage	magnet	stream	master	treats
26	**promised**	prised	drips	spread	prose	drop
27	**residence**	nicer	inside	creed	scene	denser
28	**permanent**	tramp	preen	meant	parent	natter
29	**miserable**	blame	sable	blear	table	miles
30	**pleasantly**	antler	pleat	slant	steal	peasant

Underline one number in each set of brackets to make each sum correct.

31–33 (18, 20, 19) + (11, 14, 12) = (28, 35, 33)

34–36 (8, 6, 7) × (5, 9, 7) = (64, 63, 60)

37–41 Underline any word in which one letter appears exactly twice and another letter appears three times.

buccaneer	photographer	hippopotamus	follower
memorandum	embezzle	conscience	possession
swallow	eccentric	dependent	grasshopper

42 Which vowel appears once in **teach** and twice in **assemble**? ....

43 How many letters appear twice in **occasionally**? ....

44 Which letter in **indigenous** is nearest the beginning of the alphabet? ....

45 Which letter in **extravagance** is nearest the end of the alphabet? ....

46 How many different letters are there in **rhododendron**? ....

Two of the pairs of words on each line have opposite meanings. One pair are not related in that way. Underline that pair.

47	proper/improper	tidy/untidy	take/mistake
48	valuable/invaluable	kind/unkind	popular/unpopular
49	audible/inaudible	possible/impossible	sent/dissent
50	known/unknown	patch/dispatch	own/disown
51	miss/dismiss	opened/unopened	usual/unusual
52	press/impress	agree/disagree	fasten/unfasten
53	disconnect/connect	sane/insane	verse/converse

In each space write the missing letters or numbers.

54	az	by	cx	....	ev	fu
55	bd	bf	bh	....	bl	bn
56	pon	rqp	tsr	....	xwv	zyx
57	dbc	fde	hfg	....	ljk	nlm
58	bz	ey	hx	....	nv	qu
59	b2d	c3e	d4f	....	f6h	g7i

60 Tim had a jigsaw which had 300 pieces. It took him $2\frac{1}{2}$ hours to complete it. What was the average number of pieces he put in per minute? ....

61 If the alphabet was divided into 2 equal parts, how many vowels would there be in the first half? ....

62 How many consonants would there be in the second half of the alphabet? ....

24

Underline the word which rhymes with the word on the left.

63	**forfeit**	feat	fate	lit	forget
64	**laid**	late	weighed	said	side
65	**wide**	width	widow	beside	height
66	**receipt**	recipe	receive	conscript	feat
67	**believe**	weave	belief	leaf	live
68	**calm**	firm	turn	harm	ham
69	**yacht**	catch	fetch	pat	hot
70	**persuade**	said	fade	head	lead

What must the word on the left have?

71	car	(garage, engine, radio, clock)
72	river	(boats, fish, water, bridge)
73	school	(chalk, blackboards, desks, pupils)
74	garden	(grass, hedge, soil, tree)
75	chair	(cover, arms, seat, cushion)
76	house	(chimneys, roof, furniture, curtains)
77	piano	(stool, locks, keys, music)

Andrew and Mark together had 18 sweets. Mark and Chris together had 22 sweets. Together the three boys had 30 sweets.

78–80 Andrew had ...., Mark had .... and Chris ....

81 How many sweets must Chris give Andrew if they are all to have the same number of sweets? ....

cm

Look at this graph which shows the heights of some boys. Calculate the scale to which it is drawn, and then give the height of each boy.

82 Jason is .... cm

83 Ian is .... cm

84 Justin is .... cm

85 Tom is .... cm

86 Simon is .... cm

87 Gary is .... cm

88 How much taller is Jason than Ian? ....

89 Simon is .... cm taller than Tom.

90 How much shorter is Gary than Ian? ....

In a certain code, **stream** is written **145327**. In the same code, what would these numbers represent?

91 7214 ....

92 254 ....

93 7324 ....

94 3241 ....

95 5314 ....

96 45331 ....

97 721435 ....

3 rubbers and 2 ballpoints cost 70p
6 rubbers and 2 ballpoints cost £1·00

98 I rubber costs   ....

99 I ballpoint costs   ....

100 What is the smallest number which, when divided by 2, 3 or 4, has a remainder of 1?   ....

Paper 6

On each line there are two words which have similar meanings. Underline both the words.

1-2	contract	conspire	expand	convince	enlarge
3-4	sometimes	frequently	never	often	ever
5-6	expensive	price	cheap	costly	money
7-8	fire	smoke	cook	heat	conflagration

One number in each line is incorrect. Underline it, and then write the correct number in the space at the end of the line.

9	100	81	64	48	36	25	....
10	49	58	66	76	85		....
11	941	852	763	674	586		....
12	7	15	25	31	43	51	61	....

Sort out these jumbled questions, and then answer them at the end of the line.

13 opposite is what the accept the word of? ....
14 goat what is called young of a the? ....
15 patron is who Wales saint of the? ....
16 comes Thursday and which Tuesday between day? ....

Choose a word from the column on the right of the page to complete each of these expressions.

17 To look for a .... in a haystack   dogs
18 Make .... while the sun shines   needle
19 Let sleeping .... lie   goose
20 A cock and .... story   gander
21 A wild .... chase   hay
22 What is sauce for the goose is sauce for the ....   bull

23 Write the letters of the word **ostrich** in the order in which they appear in the dictionary. ....
24 Which letter appears twice in **immigrant**, once in **prime** and not at all in **melancholy**? ....

Put the following words in alphabetical order.

    douse   double   down   dove   doubt   dough   dour

25 Which would be the middle word? ....
26 The last word? ....
27 The second word? ....

28 I put my watch right at 9 a.m. today. If it loses 1 minute every three hours what time will it show at 9 p.m. tomorrow?   ....

29 If you wrote the numbers 1 to 100 how many times would you use the figure 5?   ....

Use a word from the column on the right of the page to complete each line.

30 The woman, who was badly ...., was unable to stand up.

31 The clock, which had ...., needed rewinding.

32 The girl, who ran downstairs, ... over the stool.

33 The flowers, which hadn't been ...., were drooping sadly.

34 The clothes, which had been .... by the wind, were quite dry.

35 The vase, which had .... over, was smashed to pieces.

36 The man, who walked slowly, ... the bus.

37 The boy, who had long legs, ... over the gate easily.

jumped
watered
fallen
blown
missed
injured
tripped
stopped

Complete the following.

38 A s..........re has four sides.

39 He cycled to school in a few m..........tes.

40 We followed the rec..........e in making the cake.

41 There was a se..........h for the escaped prisoner.

42 The sh..........p is a very small fish.

43 My c..........in is the daughter of my aunt.

44 A br..........h is part of a tree.

The words on each line follow a pattern. Look for it and then complete each line.

45 hare   hear   hate   heat   feel   ....
46 lose   sole   sent   nest   went   ....
47 tales   stale   anger   range   trips   ....
48 saloon   son   modern   men   diving   ....
49 stream   mart   velour   rule   draper   ....
50 gambol   goal   carrot   coat   magnet   ....
51 threw   wet   tapes   set   groan   ....

52 Underline the middle word in order of speed.
    marched   crawled   ran   walked   sauntered

Choose from the column on the right of the page a word which is associated with a word on the left.

53	rough and		only
54	all and		tumble
55	time and		go
56	rack and		sundry
57	one and		tongs
58	hammer and		again
59	touch and		ruin
60	over and		over

61 How many letters are there in the alphabet before the third vowel?

....

62 How many letters are there are in the alphabet after the fifth vowel?

....

Can you sort out the jumbled words?

63–70 It was Amanda's birthday and she had asked **vlrseea** ....
friends to tea. Dad had made a lovely fruit **aadls** .... which
had **craoptis** ...., **groanes** .... and
chaspee .... in it. There was a **glear** .... cake with
veeenl .... candles on it. They enjoyed the
asasueg .... rolls most of all.

Forty children did four tests. This chart shows their marks.

Subject	Marks					
	0–29	30–44	45–54	55–64	65–74	75+
English	4	9	5	8	7	7
Mathematics	7	8	5	9	7	4
Geography	2	7	7	10	8	6
History	4	4	8	7	9	8

71 In English, how many children had fewer than 45 marks? ....
72 In Mathematics, how many had more than 64 marks? ....
73 In Geography, ... children gained between 45 and 64 marks.
74 In History, how many children had more than 54 marks? ....
75 In which subject did the most children have fewer than 45 marks?

....

Key

Line	
Victoria line	
Central line	
Circle line	
District line	
Metropolitan line	
Northern line	
Bakerloo line	
Piccadilly line	
Jubilee line	

76 If you are at Piccadilly Circus and want to go to Hyde Park Corner you would travel on the .... line.

77 How many stations would you pass through? ....

78 Piccadilly Circus and Oxford Circus are on the .... line.

79 Piccadilly Circus is the next station to Leicester Square on the .... line.

80 Bond Street and Oxford Circus are both on the .... line.

81 88 × 25

....

82 164 × 25

....

83 288 × 25

....

84 364 × 25

....

Here is part of a chart showing distances between large cities.

	Montreal	New York
Amsterdam	5506 km	5850 km
Brussels	5555 km	5885 km
Cairo	8729 km	9017 km

85 What is the distance between Amsterdam and New York? .... km

86 Between Cairo and Montreal there is a distance of .... km

87 There are .... km between Brussels and New York.

88 There are .... km between Cairo and New York.

89 The distance between Amsterdam and Montreal is .... km

In a restaurant it is usual for 10% of the bill to be added as a service charge. What would be the service charge on these bills?

90 £8·90 ....

91 £20·50 ....

92 £11·80 ....

93 £36·60 ....

94 £12·40 ....

95 £40·40 ....

Here is part of a bus timetable.

Manchester Bus Station	09.05
Manchester Airport	09.27
Runcorn	09.55
Ellesmere Port	10.23
Chester Zoo	10.35
Chester Bus Station	10.45

96 How long does it take to travel between Manchester and Chester Bus Stations? ....

97 The shortest distance is between (Manchester Bus Station and Manchester Airport, Manchester Airport and Runcorn, Ellesmere Port and Chester Zoo, Chester Zoo and Chester Bus Station)

98 How much longer does it take to get from Manchester Bus Station to Manchester Airport, than it does to get from Chester Zoo to Chester Bus Station? ....

99 How much less than half an hour does it take to get from Runcorn to Ellesmere Port? ....

100 From Ellesmere Port to Chester Zoo is .... minutes less than $\frac{1}{4}$ hour.

On each line there are two pairs of words which are opposites. One pair are not. Underline that pair.

1	often/seldom	many/few	great/big ✗
2	uppermost/top ✓	quiet/noisy	minute/huge
3	buy/sell	bridge/river ✓	profit/loss
4	yours/mine	theirs/ours	my/mine ✓
5	time/watch ✓	climb/descend	give/take
6	speak/listen	generous/mean	angry/cross ✓
7	divide/multiply	throw/catch	heat/cook ✓

Here are some words which have also been written in code. Look at them carefully because the code numbers may not be beneath the right words.

shoe	show	whose	sow	rose
5762	562	8651	5761	27651

Write what the code should be for these words.

8 shoe 5761   9 whose 27651
10 sow 562   11 show 5762
12 rose 8651

In the same code how would these words be written?

13 shower 576218   14 horror 768868

On each line there are two words which are associated with the word on the left. Underline these words.

15–16	**clock**	head	hands	thumbs	face	legs ✓
17–18	**coal**	mine	ours	your	vase	pit ✓
19–20	**book**	attendant	page	flower	leaf	pot ✓

Underline the correct word in each set of brackets.

21 Safe as (bells, rocks, houses, streets, horses) ✓
22 Cool as a (ice, cucumber, velvet, water, bone) ✓
23 Flat as a (fiddle, feather, needle, pancake, waffle) ✓
24 Happy as a (sandboy, new pin, honey, play, baby) ✓
25 Quick is (life, lightning, running, winking, train) ✓
26 Clear as (glass, bell, steel, mirror, crystal) ✓
27 Dull as (death, school, wet day, ditchwater, doorpost) ✗

28 Write the letter which appears most often in **international**, and after it write the letter which follows it in the alphabet. N.O. ✓

Underline the word which has the same meaning as the word on the left.

29 **replete**   replied   full   refuse   pull   repast
30 **edible**   edifice   ending   enormous   eatable   drinkable
31 **succulent**   juicy   frugal   childlike   dry   burnt
32 **derelict**   artificial   ancient   adjoining   abandoned   let
33 **indolent**   idol   lazy   lifeless   lacking   longing
34 **surmise**   guess   surmount   surround   gossip   surface
35 **monotony**   once   morsel   sameness   monument   verse

Which numbers are represented by these Roman numerals?

36 LXV = *65*   37 XLIV = *44*   38 LXXII = *72*

Change the following numbers to Roman numerals.

39 39 = *XXXIX*   40 44 = *XLIV*   41 63 = *LXIII*

Use a word which rhymes with the word on the left to complete each sentence.

42 toys   The course for the rowing event was marked with ....
43 meet   They bought a .... of furniture.
44 fire   The .... sang the school song.
45 set   She was glad to pay off the ....
46 cuff   There was a storm and the sea was very ....

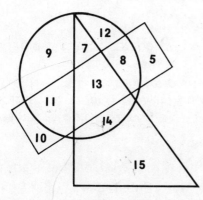

47 From the sum of the numbers in the triangle but not in the rectangle, take the sum of the numbers in the rectangle but not in the circle.
....

48 Find the sum of the numbers in the rectangle but not in the triangle, and the numbers in the circle but not in the rectangle. ....

49 From the sum of the numbers in the circle but not in the triangle, take the sum of the numbers in the rectangle but not in the triangle.
....

33

Find a word which could be put in front of each of the other words on the line to make a compound word or a phrase.

50	bow	fall	proof	water	....
51	house	ship	hearted	weight	....
52	paper	foil	plate	smith	....
53	breast	Cross	Indian	Admiral	....
54	board	mail	bird	currant	....

Underline the word which has an opposite meaning to the word on the left.

55	**absent**	away	lost	out	present	gone
56	**fresh**	stale	bread	new	baked	cooked
57	**lead**	dog	collar	follow	front	van
58	**cloudy**	sky	clear	rain	mist	fog
59	**final**	end	finish	letter	post	initial
60	**verse**	rhyme	poetry	ode	prose	limerick
61	**obtuse**	angle	wide	acute	right	size

62 Put an **a** in the space by the largest of the numbers on the right of the page.

63 Put a **b** in the space by the smallest number.

64 Put a **c** by the number which is a multiple of 5.

65 Put a **d** by the number which is divisible by 4.

66 Put an **e** by the number which is a multiple of 11.

67 Put an **f** by the number which is divisible by 9.

122 711 ....
121 446 ....
121 524 ....
122 455 ....
122 474 ....
121 349 ....

Can you work out what these jumbled words should be?

68–74 The movement of **leepop** .... and goods from one place to another is called **aotrnsrtp** .... It moves along recognised **stoure** .... such as **adors** ...., railways, **acalns** ...., shipping lanes and airways. Good roads are most important. To **deeps** .... the flow of traffic special motorways have been **tiulb** ....

Often we "round off" numbers. Instead of saying that 7681 people went to a match we say that there were 8000 there. This is rounding off to the nearest thousand. If a number is half-way between two other numbers we take it as being nearer the larger number.

What are these numbers to the nearest ten?

75 17

....

76 33

....

77 59

....

78 75

....

34

lighten   brighten   fatten   soften

If these four words are spelled backwards and then put into alphabetical order, which will be:
79 the second? ....
80 the third? ....

official   essential   comical   biblical

If these four words are spelled backwards and then put into alphabetical order, which will be:
81 the first? ....
82 the last? ....

83 68 × 25   84 84 × 25   85 288 × 25   86 164 × 25

    ....

You are in London and you want to telephone three friends in Chester.
First you must dial 051, and then, for 4 figure numbers 0244
                    for 5 figure numbers 41
                    for 6 figure numbers 8
Lastly, you dial the person's own number.

You want to telephone the numbers listed below. Give the complete number you would dial for each.
87 Chester 234567

    ....

88 Chester 9876

    ....

89 Chester 13579

    ....

Here is a list of some big cities and their populations. Number them according to size starting with the largest.

90	Liverpool	528 000	....
91	London	6 970 000	....
92	Birmingham	1 041 000	....
93	Leeds	729 000	....
94	Glasgow	809 000	....
95	Sheffield	544 000	....

This chart shows certain facts about the climate in Hawaii.

	Average day temperature	Average hours of sunshine (daily)	Average monthly rainfall
April	25°C	9·0	290 mm
May	27°C	9·3	216 mm
June	28°C	9·5	170 mm
July	29°C	10·0	244 mm
August	29°C	9·0	270 mm
September	29°C	8·5	254 mm

96 Which month has the lowest temperature? ....
97 .... has the most sunshine.
98 .... has the most rain.
99 If you could go there for a holiday the best month to go would be

....

100 The worst month would be ....

Paper 8

Complete the following proverbs by writing a word from the column on the right in each space.

1 A cat may look at a ....   sleeping
2 Too many .... spoil the broth.   vessels
3 .... makes the heart grow fonder.   stitch
4 Empty .... make the most noise.   cooks
5 Let .... dogs lie.   king
6 Jack of all trades, ... of none.   absence
7 A .... in time saves nine.   master

8 When I added 2 to a number it was then half of a half of 12. What is the number? ....
9 Which letter of the word **parcel** has the same place in the alphabet as it does in the word? ....
10 If the letters of the word **fatigue** were put in alphabetical order which would be the middle letter? ....

Underline the word on each line which cannot be formed from the word on the left, using each letter once only.

11	**defendant**	deaf	fended	defeat	defer	faded
12	**distribute**	tribes	striped	brides	trust	utter
13	**considerate**	trace	creed	crate	tread	inside
14	**partridge**	trip	pride	greed	drear	drape
15	**carpenter**	creep	trace	enact	crate	tender
16	**serendipity**	pride	endorse	trends	spirit	density
17	**prosperity**	sport	proper	spite	trot	spire

Underline the word in each line which is the "odd one out".

18	tumbler	urn	vase	glass	purse
19	inside	border	edge	rim	fringe
20	stable	tent	nest	sty	den
21	hero	monk	nun	lord	earl
22	leaps	roars	bounds	runs	swings

Emma's birthday is on March 29th. Lucy's birthday is 5 days after Emma's, and Peter's is 4 weeks before Emma's.

23 Lucy's birthday is on ....
24 Peter's is on ....

Complete the following expressions by underlining one word in each set of brackets.

25 A wet (washing, blanket, sheet, cloth, dog)
26 All (whole, ends, heads, ears, noses)
27 Good for (something, appearances, nothing, evil, work)
28 Blow one's own (nose, wind, recorder, balloon, trumpet)
29 Turn over a new (job, flower, leaf, book, page)
30 Send to (London, Timbuktu, Jericho, Coventry, Wales)
31 Wait till the (hens, traffic, cars, bills, cows) come home.

BBCI broadcasts non-stop from 6 a.m. on Monday until 12.05 a.m. on Tuesday.
32 How many hours and minutes is this? ....

The first word in each line can be changed into the second word in three stages, by altering one letter at a time. Fill in the gaps.

33–34	cope	....	....	host
35–36	hire	....	....	torn
37–38	hair	....	....	land
39–40	stop	....	....	item
41–42	stow	....	....	blob

Use a word which rhymes with the word on the left to complete each sentence.

43 sum   After playing in the snow Peter's hands were ....
44 mile   The .... of her dress was very modern.
45 so   The baker shaped the .... into loaves.

Choose the right word from the list on the right to complete each sentence.

46 A place where weapons are stored is an ....   tariff
47 The frame of a car is the ....   dialogue
48 Inside a nut is the ....   infantry
49 A conversation between two people is a ....   chancel
50 Duty paid on exports and imports is a ....   arsenal
51 Goods found floating after a shipwreck are ....   kernel
52 A list of articles is an ....   chassis
53 Instructions for preparing food are a ....   flotsam
54 The eastern end of a church is the ....   inventory
55 Foot soldiers are ....   recipe

Underline any of the following flower names which have an equal number of vowels and consonants.

56–57 dandelion   geranium   carnation   rose   tulip

Sir Walter Raleigh	1552–1618
Admiral Benbow	1653–1702
Lord Nelson	1758–1805
Sir Francis Drake	1540–1596
Sir Sidney Smith	1764–1840
Lord Effingham	1536–1624

58 Which of these admirals was born first? ....

59 Which was born the most recently? ....

60 How old was Lord Effingham when Raleigh was born? ....

61 How old was Sir Sidney Smith when Nelson died? ....

62 Which of these men had the longest life? ....

63 Which had the shortest life? ....

64 How old was Raleigh when Drake died? ....

65 Which of these men was alive on the centenary of the death of Drake? ....

66 Queen Victoria came to the throne in 1837. Which of these men was alive then? ....

Blind people use the braille alphabet which is a series of raised dots. Here are some of the letters of the braille alphabet.

Can you read these braille words?

67 ....

68 ....

69 ....

70 ....

71 ....

Here is part of a train timetable.

	Train 1 SO	Train 2 FO	Train 3 SX
Coventry	14.23	15.55	16.48
Birmingham Airport	14.33	16.13	16.58
Birmingham New Street	15.11	16.48	17.22
Wolverhampton	15.28	17.06	17.47
Stafford	15.50	17.22	18.06

SO = Saturdays only
FO = Fridays only
SX = not Saturdays

72 How long does it take Train 1 to travel from Coventry to Stafford?

....

73 Train 2 takes ....
74 Train 3 takes ....
75 How many of these trains travel on Saturdays? (1, 2, 3)
76 How many of these trains travel on Fridays? (1, 2, 3)
77 How many of these trains travel on Wednesdays? (1, 2, 3)

Can you work out what the next two numbers in each line should be?

78–79 $\frac{1}{2}$ $\frac{1}{4}$ $\frac{1}{8}$ $\frac{1}{16}$ $\frac{1}{32}$ ....
80–81 1 1 2 3 5 8 13 21 34 ....

The contents list to part of an encyclopaedia reads as follows:

	Page
Famous people and events	2
Explorations and discoveries	59
British Prime Ministers	65
Kings and Queens of England	67
Presidents of the U.S.A.	69

To find out about the following people I would turn to page:

82 Francis Drake ....
83 George Washington ....
84 Julius Caesar ....
85 Harold Wilson ....
86 Queen Victoria ....
87 Christopher Columbus ....
88 Horatio Nelson ....

tennis golf good beach sailing children's activities

Blue Sea Hotel

Queen's Hotel

Hotel Lido

Eden Rock Hotel

Beach Hotel

Park Hotel

This picture shows you the amenities offered in several hotels.

89 Which hotel offers tennis, golf and sailing? ....

90 How many hotels offer sailing and children's activities? (1, 2, 3, 4, 5, 6)

91 Which hotel offers golf, children's activities and a good beach?

....

92 How many offer tennis and children's activities? (1, 2, 3, 4, 5, 6)

93 How many offer golf, sailing and a good beach? (1, 2, 3, 4, 5, 6)

In each of the sets below there is one word which does not fit in with the others. Underline it:

94	emotion	95	depart	96	indiscreet
	reason		quit		reckless
	purpose		arrive		careful
	motive		leave		rash

	Key
Victoria line	⬛⬛⬛⬛⬛⬛⬛
Central line	⬛⬛⬛⬛⬛⬛⬛
Circle line	══════
District line	∧∧∧∧∧∧
Metropolitan line	▨▨▨▨
Northern line	▬▬▬▬
Bakerloo line	▮▯▮▯▮
Piccadilly line	▥▥▥▥
Jubilee line	▮▯▮▯▮

97 I want to go from Bond Street to Knightsbridge. They are not on the same line. Where would be the best place to change?

....

98 The first part of my journey would be on the .... line.

99 The second part of my journey would be on the .... line.

100 Name the station I would pass through on this line.

....

42

If the statement is true write **t** in the space; if it is false write **f.**

1　The equator divides the world into two equal sections.　..........
2　At the beginning of British Summer Time clocks are put back one hour.　..........
3　November is a longer month than March.　..........
4　We live in the nineteenth century.　..........
5　768 BC was earlier than 678 BC.　..........
6　1990 is a leap year.　..........

Find the letter which will best end the first word and start the second word.

7　gran .... aily　　8　wis .... ard　　9　tre .... ven
10　curv .... very　　11　ter .... ice　　12　bat .... ard

13–14　Smile is to happiness as (frown, tear, laugh) is to (whisper, laughter, sorrow)

15–16　Food is to hunger as (drink, water, bread) is to (eat, thirst, cold)

17–18　4 is to 1 as (2, 3, 1) is to ($\frac{1}{4}$, $\frac{3}{8}$, $\frac{5}{8}$)

Underline the correct meaning of the following expressions.

19　**To save one's face**
　　To use make-up
　　To avoid disgrace
　　To use a sun hat
　　To always do well

20　**Dead beat**
　　Music without rhythm
　　A dead policeman
　　To take things easily
　　Exhausted

21　**To throw in the towel**
　　To put the towel in the washing machine
　　To do a little extra work
　　To clean up
　　To give up

22　**To have too many irons in the fire**
　　To try too many things at the same time
　　To get the iron too hot
　　To burn the ironing
　　To take advantage of someone

Choose a word from the column on the right of the page to complete each sentence.

23 The secretary was .... and the office was well organised.

24 The lady made a .... saying that the dress had shrunk.

25 A .... arose when they all wanted the same book.

26 It is always nice to be paid a ....

27 On .... of the work the men were paid.

28 Oxygen is a .... of water.

29 An angle of 20° is the .... of an angle of 70°.

compliment
completion
component
complement
complication
complaint
competent

30 Mr. Old was born in 1897 and died in 1965. How old was he when he died?   ....

Underline the correct answer.

31 My aunt is (my sister's mother, my brother's wife, my father's sister, my daughter's mother)

32 My cousin is (my sister's child, my aunt's child, my grandmother's niece, my mother's sister)

33 My uncle is (my father's brother, my brother's son, my father's father, my brother's cousin)

34 My grandfather is (my uncle's brother, my brother's father, my father's father, my brother's uncle)

Mr. Welloff goes to the bank to cash a cheque for £68·99$\frac{1}{2}$. He asks to be given the money in such a way that he has the smallest possible number of £5 notes, £1 notes and coins.

35–41   How was he given his money?

.... £5 notes	.... £1 notes
.... 50p coins	.... 20p coins
.... 10p coins	.... 5p coins
.... 2p coins	.... 1p coins
.... $\frac{1}{2}$p coins	

Underline the "odd one out" in each line.

42	sing	song	shout	hum	call
43	desert	leave	pursue	forsake	abandon
44	Mersey	Snowdon	Dee	Thames	Severn
45	stare	gaze	glance	hear	watch
46	tap	rap	stride	strike	knock

Underline a number in each set of brackets to make the sum correct.

47–49 (11, 9, 5) × (4, 7, 6) = (54, 55, 56)

50–52 (14, 11, 13) − (8, 7, 5) = (10, 8, 2)

Underline the pair of words which do not have similar meanings.

53	behaviour/conduct	disease/sickness	many/few
54	level/even	latitude/longitude	hide/conceal
55	initial/final	avoid/elude	clasp/hug
56	ally/helper	asleep/awake	last/end
57	bad/evil	decrease/reduce	ebb/flow
58	force/compel	live/die	loose/release
59	prose/verse	lasting/durable	enemy/foe

Write a word in the space which satisfies the definition, and which rhymes with the word on the left.

60	see	A place where ships are unloaded	....
61	dim	We sing this at church and at school	....
62	rout	A shortage of rain	....
63	him	A part of the body	....
64	how	A part of a tree	....
65	home	We use this to tidy our hair	....
66	mist	Part of an arm	....

67 How many minutes are there in a Thursday?   ....

One word can be used for each pair of definitions.

68 Frozen rain
To call from afar   (...................)

69 Grumble
A game bird   (...................)

70 A spike of corn
Part of the head   (...................)

71 Healthy
Oil is obtained from one   (...................)

72 A season
To leap   (...................)

73 A locomotive
To instruct   (...................)

74 We stick it on a letter
To tread heavily   (...................)

Fill in the missing figures in the following sums.

75–78
```
    2 7 4 5
    3 ... 4 ...
 + ... 8 ... 7
 ────────────
    9 2 6 1
```

79–81
```
    ... ... 3 5
 ×        ....
 ────────────
    6 8 1 0
```

82–85
```
    3 ... 5 ...
 ×          9
 ────────────
    2 ... 4 ... 3
```

This chart shows how many records these groups sold each week in October.

	1st week	2nd week	3rd week	4th week
The Fudgers	28 000	25 000	24 000	25 000
The Grunters	35 000	32 000	43 000	42 000
The Hoppers	27 000	26 000	23 000	22 000
The Jackdaws	38 000	42 000	41 000	39 000
King Kong	24 000	27 000	36 000	48 000

86 Which group was top in two successive weeks? ....

87 Which group sold more each week? ....

88 Which group sold fewer each week? ....

89 .... rose from bottom to top in 4 weeks.

90 .... sold the fewest records altogether.

91 Which group sold most in the first two weeks? ....

92 Which group sold most in the second two weeks? ....

10% is another way of saying $\frac{1}{10}$, so 20% must be $\frac{2}{10}$ or $\frac{1}{5}$.
Find 20% of:

93 45   94 30   95 60   96 75   97 £5·50

....

Telephoning in an emergency

      1   Call the operator by dialling 999.
      2   Tell the operator which service you want: Fire, Police or
      Ambulance.
      3   Wait until the Emergency Service answers.
      4   Give the full address of the place where help is needed and any
      other information they ask for.

98 You should (tell the operator where help is needed,
    tell her which of the services you need, dial the number she gives
    you)
99 In the telephone directory you are told how to dial 999 without looking
    at the numbers. This is (because it is clever to do this, because it is
    easier to do it without looking, in case you have to do it in the dark)
100 When the Emergency Service answers you should (give them your
    name, tell them where you want help, tell them how the accident
    happened)

From the letters of the word **prosperous**, form words with the given meanings. Use each letter once only.

1 Correct ....
2 Riders use these ....
3 Part of a meal ....
4 We keep money in it ....
5 To go against ....
6 An old-fashioned name for a husband or wife ....

Find the two letters which will best end the first word and start the second word.

7 purp........ague   8 mosa........icle
9 bran........arge   10 plur........most
11 peri........ield   12 fast........gine

Underline the correct definition.

13 At the eleventh hour

At the darkest time of night
To go to bed late
At the last moment
Too late to be any good

14 To split hairs

To comb out tangles in one's hair
To argue over trifles
To have one's hair cut
To make a cutting remark

15 If we reduced the number of minutes in an hour to 40 how many hours would there be in a day? ....

Choose the right word from the list on the right to fill each space.

father   **young**

16 swan   ....   fawn
17 hare   ....   cub
18 stallion   ....   cygnet
19 gander   ....   kid
20 stag   ....   leveret
21 goat   ....   foal
22 bear   ....   gosling

House of Plantaganet	Reign
Henry II	1154–1189
Richard I	1189–1199
John	1199–1216
Henry III	1216–1272
Edward I	1272–1307
Edward II	1307–1327
Edward III	1327–1377
Richard II	1377–1399

23 Which of these kings reigned for the longest time? ....

24 Which king reigned for the shortest time? ....

25 For how long did the Plantaganets reign? ....

26 Which king was ruling England at the beginning of the thirteenth century? ....

27 The Black Death was in 1348 and 1349. Who was king then?
....

28 The Model Parliament met in 1295. Who was king then?
....

29 Who was on the throne at the beginning of the fourteenth century?
....

Can you think of a word which can be put in front of the other words on the line to form a compound word or a phrase?

30	bar	jug	maid	chocolate	....
31	master	light	dress	quarters	....
32	paste	ache	brush	powder	....
33	writing	kerchief	shake	cuff	....
34	nail	tip	print	mark	....
35	ball	path	step	print	....

Complete the following proverbs by using a word from the column on the right-hand side of the page.

36	.... is the best policy.	success
37	Many .... make light work.	birds
38	Nothing succeeds like	hay
39	Practice makes	lining
40	Make .... while the sun shines.	honesty
41	Every cloud has a silver	action
42	Spare the rod and spoil the	perfect
43	Kill two .... with one stone.	hands
44	.... speaks louder than words.	child

The first word in each line can be changed into the second word in three stages, by altering one letter at a time. Fill in the gaps.

45–46	wide	....	....	sing
47–48	hoot	....	....	boar
49–50	take	....	....	mine
51–52	hill	....	....	mole

Underline the word which is in some way different from the others.

53	call	summon	proclaim	cry	conceal	declare
54	durable	firm	weak	lasting	enduring	permanent
55	entire	complete	whole	part	intact	unbroken
56	enemy	foe	adversary	opponent	antagonist	colleague
57	singular	strange	plural	odd	peculiar	unique

If a statement is true write **t** in the space; if it is false write **f**.

58 Five 50p pieces have the same value as twenty-five 10p pieces.
....

59 December 26th is Christmas Day.   ....

60 If January 14th is a Wednesday then the previous Thursday was January 7th.   ....

61 If New Year's Day is on a Thursday the last day of January is a Saturday.   ....

62 New York is the capital of the U.S.A.   ....

63 April and September both have 31 days.   ....

64 A decade is a period of 20 years.   ....

Here is a list of the average daily hours of sunshine in Manchester. They are written very accurately. Can you write them to the nearest whole number of hours?

65	April	5·1	....
66	May	7·5	....
67	June	3·9	....
68	July	4·0	....
69	August	3·8	....
70	September	4·3	....
71	October	2·7	....

Here are the marks fifty children received in four tests.

Subject	Marks					
	0–29	30–44	45–54	55–64	65–74	75+
English	6	11	9	8	9	7
French	4	10	12	9	10	5
Mathematics	6	9	14	7	8	6
Science	8	12	11	8	7	4

72   How many children had fewer than 45 marks in Mathematics?

....

73   .... children had more than 54 marks in Science.

74   In French how many had between 30 and 64 marks?   ....

75   .... children had more than 64 marks in English.

76   The biggest group in the under 45 marks set was in   ....

Three people went to a restaurant, and had the set menu.
It was:

~MENU~

Soup	35p
Plaice	£2·70
Vegetables	45p
Ice cream	40p
Coffee	30p

Complete this bill for the three of them.

£ p

77   Soup   ....

78   Fish   ....

79   Vegetables   ....

80   Ice cream   ....

81   Coffee   ....
                     _____

82   ....

83   10% service charge   ....
                     _____

84   ....

Mrs. Scott was born in 1942. Her daughter was born when she was 27, and her son was born three years previously.

85 In which year was Mrs. Scott's daughter born? ....

86 Her son was born in ....

87 How old will the son be when Mrs. Scott is 60? ....

Look at this map.

88 There are a stately home and a church in ....

89 There is just a stately home (no gardens to view) at ....

90 There is an observatory at ....

91 Capesthorne is on which road? ....

92 Jodrell Bank is on the ....

93 There is just a church at ....

This chart shows the distances between various cities.

	Dublin	Geneva	Madrid
London	449 km	753 km	1246 km
New York	5103 km	6201 km	5763 km
Paris	782 km	409 km	1054 km
Rome	1905 km	715 km	1358 km

94 How far is it from London to Madrid?   ....
95 It is .... from Paris to Geneva.
96 The longest distance between two cities is
    from ....
97 The shortest distance is between ....
98 It is .... from Madrid to Paris.
99 Which is the longer distance? (Rome to Geneva, Paris to Dublin)
100 From Rome to Madrid is ....

Paper 11

Choose a word from the list on the right to fill each space.

1. Dad was very annoyed and it was difficult to .... him.

2. The lion catches and eats other animals; it is a .... creature.

3. Our car was stuck in a snowdrift. Should we wait for help to arrive or should we start walking? It was a ....

4. We decided to play football, a game in which we could all ....

5. A sponge soaks up water; it is made of a .... material.

6. Balanced on the handlebars of his bicycle, the clown was in a .... position.

7. He was knocked out in one of the .... rounds.

participate
predicament
precarious
porous
placate
preliminary
predatory

My watch is 8 minutes fast, and the bus which should have arrived at 4.32 p.m. is 6 minutes late.

8. What time does my watch show when the bus arrives? ....

Anne and Emma learn Spanish and French; Emma and Lucy learn French and German. Caroline and Anne learn Welsh and Spanish.

9. Who learns French but not German? ....

10. Who learns Spanish but not Welsh? ....

11. Which language doesn't Anne learn? ....

12. Which language doesn't Emma learn? ....

13. How many of the girls learn three languages? ....

On each line there are two words which have similar meanings.
Underline these words.

14-15	walker	pedlar	scene	pedestrian	sight
16-17	full	vacant	let	empty	go
18-19	narrate	entice	design	investigate	recite

Write the following numbers in Roman numerals.

20. 165

21. 209

....

....

22. 414

23. 388

....

....

54

24 Two months of the year begin with the 13th letter of the alphabet. Write the second letter of the month that is between them. ....

Write a word which matches the definition, and which also rhymes with the word on the left.

25 poke   Part of an egg   ....
26 mat   An insect   ....
27 pile   Part of a church   ....
28 mains   Our blood travels in these   ....
29 lane   Part of a bridle   ....

From the letters of the word **discriminate** form new words having the following meanings.

30 To cut into small pieces   ....
31 A packing case   ....
32 Boiling water produces this   ....
33 Digger of coal   ....
34 Wrong-doing often punished by imprisonment   ....

35 If **deaf** contains the 6th letter of the alphabet write **x** unless **cadge** contains the 7th letter in which case write **z**. ....

Complete the following proverbs by choosing a word from the column on the right.

36 Where there's a will there's a ....   mile
37 When the cat's away the mice will ....   mind
38 There are two sides to every ....   robbery
39 Out of sight, out of ....   basket
40 A friend in need is a friend ....   way
41 A miss is as good as a ....   question
42 Don't put all your eggs in one ....   play
43 Fair exchange is no ....   indeed

One number in each line is wrong. Underline that number, and write the correct number in the space at the end of the line.

44	168	156	143	132	120	108	....
45	3	7	14	18	25	33	....
46	4	8	9	12	13	16	....
47	827	726	645	554	463	372	....
48	192	283	374	455	556	647	....
49	11	15	14	18	17	20	....

55

John's birthday is in the month after the month which starts with the 15th letter of the alphabet.

50 In which month was John born? ....

Use all the letters of each word on the left to form a new word with the given meaning.

51	present	A snake	....
52	ocean	A small boat	....
53	wolves	A part of the alphabet	....
54	drawer	Person in charge of prisoners	....
55	tutor	A fish	....
56	pastel	a fastener made of bent wire	....
57	trestle	Brought by the postman	....

One word on each line cannot be formed from the letters of the word on the left, using each letter once only. Underline that word.

58	**endorsement**	stored	deter	order	drone	storm
59	**parliament**	temper	plain	lament	ailment	trail
60	**deliverance**	clean	creed	anvil	driver	leader
61	**descendant**	scene	decant	scant	tended	tandem
62	**representative**	instep	interest	string	rest	entire
63	**conversation**	store	version	inverse	stance	scooter

Put these words into alphabetical order.

furrow   fuse   further   fuss   furniture   fury   furnace

64 Which is the middle word? ....

65 Which is the last word? ....

66 Which is the first word? ....

67 Write the time which is 2 hours 50 minutes later than 10.35 p.m.

....

68 Write the time which is 3 hours 15 minutes earlier than 9.35 a.m.

....

On each line there is a sum which does not have the same answer as the sum in the left-hand column. Underline that sum.

69	$63 \div 7$	$(3 \times 3 \times 1)$	$(4 \times 2) + 1$	$(5 \times 2) \times 1$
70	$84 \div 12$	$(1 + 2 + 4)$	$(3 \times 3) - 1$	$(4 \times 2) - 1$
71	$108 \div 9$	$(3 \times 4) + 1$	$(11 \times 1) + 1$	$(2 \times 7) - 2$
72	$121 \div 11$	$(3 \times 3) + 2$	$(100 \div 10) - 1$	$(2 \times 4) + 3$
73	$56 \div 7$	$(64 \div 8)$	$(40 \div 5)$	$(28 \div 4)$

Here are some counties of England, with their county towns, areas and populations.

County	County town	Area in km	Population
Avon	Bristol	1346	920 000
Cheshire	Chester	2328	930 000
Norfolk	Norwich	5335	690 000
Suffolk	Ipswich	3807	602 000
Merseyside	Liverpool	646	1 521 000
Cornwall	Truro	3546	422 000

74 Which is the county town of the county with the smallest area?
....

75 Which is the county town of the county with the largest area?
....

76 Which is the county town of the county with the smallest population?
....

77 Which county has the largest population? ....

78 The area of Suffolk is ....

79–80 Which two counties have a difference of 10 000 in their populations?
....

Here is a chart which shows the number of people who stayed at Hillside Youth Hostel last year.

81 In which month did twice as many people stay there as in October?
....

82 In which month did half as many people stay there as in August?
....

83 The April and October figures put together were the same as those for
....

84 How many more people stayed there in August than in September?
....

85 How many fewer were there in May than in July? ....

86 How many fewer than 2000 stayed there altogether? ....

To send printed papers outside Europe the postal charges are:

Up to 40 g: $15\frac{1}{2}$p. Each additional 10 g (or part thereof): 4p.

What would it cost to post the following weights of package?

87 28 g ....

88 75 g ....

89 52 g ....

90 41 g ....

Here are some details about the climate in Kenya.

	Average daily temperature	Average hours of sun (daily)	Average monthly rainfall
April	30°C	7·4	195 mm
May	28°C	6·6	320 mm
June	27°C	7·5	120 mm
July	26°C	7·0	90 mm
August	26°C	8·0	65 mm
September	27°C	8·4	65 mm
October	29°C	8·6	88 mm

91 Which consecutive months have the same temperature?

....

92 Which month averages 1 hour less daily sunshine than September?

....

93–94 Two other months have the same temperature. They are

....

95 If you like it sunny and dry the best month is

....

96 If you like it sunny and dry the worst month is ....

97 Which month has the least sunshine? ....

98 If I had spent 5p more on a book I would have spent a quarter of my money. If the book cost 85p how much money did I have at first?

....

2 Beanobars and 3 Choctoffs cost 96p
2 Beanobars and 1 Choctoff cost 56p

99 1 Beanobar costs ....

100 1 Choctoff costs ....

Paper 12

1 Mrs. Oldham was born in 1891 and died in 1956. Her daughter was born when Mrs. Oldham was 28.
How old was the daughter when Mrs. Oldham died? ....

Underline the correct meaning of the following expressions.

2 **To be on tenterhooks**
To be hanging up
To be very sore
To be in suspense
To be spoilt

3 **A month of Sundays**
A month in which there are five Sundays
A leap year
A month when one is supposed to go to church
An extremely long period

4 **To see daylight**
To understand
How you feel when you wake up
What a diver sees when he comes to the surface
To be colour blind

5 **To be caught red-handed**
To be caught when you've cut your hand
To be caught doing wrong
To be caught painting your nails
To be caught playing with fire

6 **To make one's mark**
To learn to write
To mark time
To do very well indeed
To be a nuisance

Write the next number in each line.

7	924	835	746	657	568	479	....
8	7	15	9	17	11	19	....
9	3	6	7	14	15	30	....
10	21	18	19	16	17	14	....
11	2	6	4	12	6	18	....
12	5	7	10	14	15	21	....
13	1	4	9	16	25	36	....

On the left of the page are some long words, and on the right there is a column of shorter words. Can you match them for meaning?

14	**deficiency** means	hide
15	**aptitude** means	enemy
16	**copious** means	explain
17	**opulent** means	lack
18	**taciturn** means	rich
19	**secrete** means	ability
20	**reverberate** means	chew
21	**elucidate** means	much
22	**masticate** means	silent
23	**adversary** means	echo

Two pairs of words on each line have opposite meanings. One pair have not. Underline that pair.

24	order/disorder	dense/condense	use/misuse
25	regular/irregular	honest/dishonest	pact/impact
26	firm/confirm	pure/impure	content/discontent
27	real/unreal	certain/uncertain	spire/conspire
28	correct/incorrect	come/income	sufficient/insufficient
29	deed/indeed	finite/infinite	visible/invisible
30	known/unknown	fence/defence	active/inactive

Fill in the missing letters in these sentences.

31	I have a s.........t.........l for my school books.
32–33	I am a shop. I have co.........ers and sh.........es.
34	I am a camera. I take ....oto.........phs.
35	I am a barometer. I forecast the w.........t.........r.
36	I am a plumb-line. I tell if things are ve.........i.........al.

There is one word on each line which is somehow different from the others. Underline that word.

37	brays	purrs	trots	neighs	bleats
38	bind	fix	tether	loosen	join
39	cruel	strong	robust	sturdy	powerful
40	prowls	howls	frisks	flits	crawls
41	butter	yogurt	apple	cheese	cream
42	waddles	struts	flutters	hops	crows
43	howl	groan	moan	fight	grumble

Complete the following sums by filling in the missing figures.

44–46
```
   3....8 1
   ....4 6 9
 + 1 6 7 4
 ─────────
   7 9....4
 ─────────
```

47–49
```
   4........
 ×      ....
 ─────────
   3 1 9 9
 ─────────
```

50–51
```
   9 7....4
 − 2 3 8 1
 ─────────
   7....0 3
 ─────────
```

Here are some similes. Underline the correct word to make them complete.

52 As alike as two   (flowers, trees, peas, books, nuts)
53 As crooked as a   (corkscrew, fork, top, lane, monkey)
54 As dry as   (towel, cloth, cleaning, sand, dust)
55 As heavy as   (tonne, lead, weight, coal, house)
56 As stubborn as a   (horse, donkey, elephant, mule, cat)
57 As happy as a   (bird, lark, robin, joke, baby)

In the space at the end of each line write the following letters.

58	**x** beside the largest number	234 275	....
59	**y** beside the smallest number	234 943	....
60	**z** beside the number which is a multiple of 3	234 141	....
61	**b** by the number divisible by 5	224 129	....
62	**t** by the multiple of 11	234 751	....
63	**c** by the number divisible by 7	224 936	....
64	**d** by the multiple of 4	234 934	....

Think of a word which can be put in front of the other words on the line to form a compound word or a phrase.

65	ground	thing	time	wright	....
66	car	woman	force	officer	....
67	pond	cake	monger	hook	....
68	gage	house	grocer	fly	....
69	shelf	shop	marker	worm	....

Fill in the missing numbers and letters in each line.

70	1b	3d	2c	....	3d	5f
71	2b9	3c8	4d7	....	6f5	7g4
72	ba	db	fc	....	je	lf
73	az3	by4	cx5	....	ev7	fu8
74	1b3	2c4	3d5	....	5f7	6g8
75	284	375	466	....	648	739
76	bc1	ef2	hi3	....	no5	qr6

Here are some more letters written in braille.

O   P   S   T   U   V   W   Y

What are these words?

77 ....

78 ....

79 ....

80 ....

81 ....

82 ....

Here are some words written in a code, but they are mixed up. Can you sort them out?

cost	stale	least	beast
$= @ / - \times$	$- \times / = @$	$+ \times / = @$	$£ \div = @$

83 **cost** should be ....
84 **least** should be ....
85 **stale** should be ....
86 **beast** should be ....

In the same code, what are these words?

87 £/=@– × is ....
88 +÷@@– × is ....
89 £–÷= × = is ....
90 £÷++– × is ....

91–98 Can you work out what these jumbled words are?

Baked jacket potatoes

Burcs .... the potatoes, dry and **kricp** .... well with a
fork. **Shrub** .... with melted butter. **Cleap** .... on a
baking tray. **Kabe** .... till soft. When cooked cut in
flah .... and scoop out the potato. **Sham** .... well with
butter and seasoning. Replace filling and **verse** .... at once.

99 Mr. X takes 2 hours 30 minutes to do a journey at an average speed of
40 m.p.h. How far does he go? ....
100 Mr. Y. does the same journey in 2 hours. What is his average speed?
....

Paper   1   2   3   4   5   6   7   8   9   10 11 12

Total marks

100
95
90
85
80
75
70
65
60
55
50
45
40
35
30
25
20
15
10
5
0

DATE